FIND
- A -
WORD
6

Pat Duncan

Beaver Books

First published in 1983 by
The Hamlyn Publishing Group Limited
London · New York · Sydney · Toronto
Astronaut House, Feltham, Middlesex, England

© Copyright Pat Duncan 1983
ISBN 0 600 20512 6

Made and printed in Great Britain by
Hazell Watson & Viney Ltd
Aylesbury, Bucks
Set in Univers

Foreword

Here's a new collection of puzzles of the kind Find-a-Word fans know and love – with a few new twists to sharpen your wits.

If you've never seen a Find-a-Word puzzle before, here's how to solve one: all the words you want to find are hidden somewhere in the grid of letters. The word you are looking for might be read forwards, backwards, up, down or diagonally but the letters of the word form a straight line in there somewhere. All you have to do is find it and put a pencil line round it. Then you go on to the next word, which might overlap or cut across one you've already found – letters of one word can be used in another. Simple enough, but here and there it's made just a little bit trickier.

In the second part we go on to Word Mazes and Trace-outs. Different rules apply to these and they are explained at the beginning of the section, on page 74.

All the answers are at the back of the book, beginning on page 91. But have a good try before you give up and look at them.

Have fun with these.

Pat Duncan

1. Make a start

First, let's make a beginning by finding these 34 words, all connected with getting things going.

boom	force	plant
boost	gambit	prime
commence	germ	proffer
egg	ignition	promote
embark	incite	remove
encourage	morning	sign
engineer	opening	source
entrance	originate	start
evolving	outset	take
father	overture	uncover
fire	pioneer	venture
first		

P	G	E	N	C	O	U	R	A	G	E
R	E	E	N	O	I	P	L	A	N	T
O	R	O	R	M	R	E	H	T	A	F
F	E	E	P	M	G	T	R	A	T	S
F	O	T	E	E	I	A	H	K	I	I
E	I	R	I	N	N	N	M	E	G	G
R	O	R	C	C	I	I	V	B	N	N
F	V	E	E	E	N	G	N	I	I	E
I	E	V	O	L	V	I	N	G	T	T
R	R	O	S	O	U	R	C	E	I	O
S	T	C	T	S	O	O	B	O	O	M
T	U	N	E	M	B	A	R	K	N	O
E	R	U	T	N	E	V	O	M	E	R
T	E	S	T	U	O	E	M	I	R	P

2. Count your blessings

Enjoy yourself with all these good and cheerful words, 31 to find.

best
blessing
bliss
comfortable
content
dancing
delight
ecstasy
felicity
full
good

grand
helpful
high
honeymoon
joyful
liking
merrier
pleasure
rapture
rejoice

relish
revelry
roses
satisfaction
singing
solace
sparkle
spice
sun
transport

G	A	B	Y	R	E	V	E	L	R	Y
E	N	R	E	I	R	R	E	M	T	G
B	L	I	S	S	U	N	N	S	N	I
F	U	B	C	S	T	R	O	S	E	S
T	F	L	A	N	P	L	I	H	T	E
R	P	E	L	T	A	I	T	O	N	C
O	L	S	F	C	R	D	C	N	O	I
P	E	S	E	E	E	O	A	E	C	O
S	H	I	L	L	L	U	F	Y	O	J
N	G	N	I	K	I	L	S	M	G	E
A	I	G	C	R	S	O	I	O	O	R
R	H	I	I	A	H	U	T	O	O	C
T	E	N	T	P	G	R	A	N	D	N
E	R	G	Y	S	A	T	S	C	E	E

3. In the picture

Find these 28 words connected with art to put you in the picture.

artist
cartoon
cast
creation
cut
drawing
effigy
etched
form
fresco

gouache
graving
icon
limner
miniature
mosaic
pencil
photograph
picture

portrait
posing
position
purist
replica
sculpt
silhouette
vignette
watercolour

G	N	I	W	A	R	D	H	A	H	A
O	L	I	C	N	E	P	N	N	R	V
U	I	W	A	H	O	L	O	T	E	I
A	M	A	C	P	T	O	I	T	N	G
C	N	T	E	A	T	S	T	O	O	N
H	E	E	O	R	T	E	A	S	I	E
E	R	R	A	G	U	S	E	C	T	T
T	U	C	P	O	R	T	R	A	I	T
C	T	O	H	T	S	A	C	R	S	E
I	A	L	I	O	N	I	V	I	O	F
A	I	O	S	H	L	O	R	I	P	F
S	N	U	T	P	L	U	C	S	N	I
O	I	R	E	S	P	O	S	I	N	G
M	M	R	O	F	R	E	S	C	O	Y

4. Words and music

Here are 31 words to find and music is the theme.

allegro
andante
anthem
canon
cantata
canticle
chant
chorus
concerto
duet
fantasia

fugue
glee
hymn
impromptu
minuet
motet
nocturne
note
opera
oratorio

pitch
roulade
round
serenade
sonatina
study
symphony
toccata
tone
tune

T	E	U	N	I	M	E	H	T	N	A
S	A	T	A	N	A	C	D	O	L	L
N	Y	P	R	E	T	O	N	S	I	L
A	Y	M	E	I	A	A	U	O	N	E
I	D	O	P	G	C	T	O	N	E	G
S	U	R	O	H	C	A	R	A	E	R
A	T	P	Y	M	O	T	E	T	D	O
T	S	M	H	T	T	N	U	I	A	U
N	N	I	N	E	R	A	Y	N	N	L
A	F	U	G	U	E	C	D	A	E	A
F	O	L	T	D	C	A	R	T	R	D
C	E	C	H	A	N	T	O	I	E	E
E	O	R	A	T	O	R	I	O	S	N
N	R	A	E	L	C	I	T	N	A	C

5. Keeping afloat

A strange collection of vessels here to keep you afloat. See if you can find all 28.

boat	frigate	sampan
brigantine	galleon	sloop
catamaran	gig	smack
cutter	gondola	tramp
destroyer	junk	transport
dory	ketch	trawler
dreadnought	launch	trireme
felucca	liner	warship
ferry	lugger	
flagship	punt	

S	T	R	E	Y	O	R	T	S	E	D
Y	R	O	D	C	U	T	T	E	R	D
R	A	E	T	T	R	I	R	E	M	E
R	M	N	A	R	A	M	A	T	A	C
E	P	I	A	L	O	D	N	O	G	K
F	T	T	J	U	N	K	S	W	T	E
R	L	N	L	O	B	L	P	A	R	R
I	L	A	U	N	C	H	O	R	A	G
G	I	G	G	P	S	B	R	S	W	A
A	H	I	G	S	L	A	T	H	L	L
T	C	R	E	F	H	E	M	I	E	L
E	T	B	R	E	N	I	L	P	R	E
F	E	L	U	C	C	A	P	O	A	O
E	K	C	A	M	S	L	O	O	P	N

6. Royal occasion

Sail royally through these 33 names and words you might read in connection with a royal occasion.

Andrew	Cornwall	roar
Anne	coronation	robe
arms	Diana	Sandringham
Balmoral	earl	sceptre
calm	Edinburgh	smile
cars	Elizabeth	throne
castle	England	Victoria
Charles	horses	Wales
cheers	orb	wave
coach	palace	window
corgi	reign	Windsor

G	W	L	A	I	R	O	T	C	I	V
D	I	A	N	A	C	O	A	C	H	C
I	N	R	V	A	H	S	A	G	O	S
G	D	O	L	E	T	D	R	R	U	M
R	S	M	I	L	E	U	N	A	A	R
O	O	L	E	T	B	W	A	H	C	A
C	R	A	E	N	A	I	G	S	S	S
T	A	B	I	L	Z	N	R	E	E	R
H	O	D	L	I	I	D	O	L	S	E
R	E	A	O	R	L	O	A	R	R	E
O	A	N	D	R	E	W	T	A	O	H
N	D	N	A	L	G	N	E	H	H	C
E	A	E	L	P	A	L	A	C	E	A
S	C	E	P	T	R	E	I	G	N	R

7. Anagrams

These 34 strange words and phrases are anagrams of the words you want. Switch the letters round in each case to make the word you're looking for.

a deep rot

back rest

bather

can go

carthorse

cats' co

clear it

counter

cruel

fit dice

gear me

glue on

go use lie

grenade

helpers in

his leg

in arts

I strip

let read

love it

men gain

mob's role

more in tapes

newer

pave pro

port prey

ran loot

rap set

rat Eric

red age

rope lag

spotter

tour gown

trap also

T	S	O	C	C	A	A	E	S	T	W
I	W	N	U	Y	L	V	G	O	E	R
C	E	O	R	T	O	L	A	N	L	E
I	D	E	E	R	G	A	E	M	O	N
F	M	R	P	E	R	R	A	T	I	C
E	E	P	L	P	E	O	O	A	V	S
D	A	M	E	O	P	D	R	W	R	E
E	N	A	N	R	A	T	N	E	N	U
T	I	R	I	P	S	R	M	A	B	L
A	N	T	S	E	T	O	R	P	R	O
R	G	I	H	L	O	U	N	G	E	G
E	R	C	U	L	R	N	N	A	A	I
P	R	L	B	R	A	C	K	E	T	S
O	V	E	R	S	L	E	I	G	H	E

8. United Nations

All these 36 countries are in the United Nations and they're gathered together here for you to find.

Australia
Bahrain
Benin
Canada
Chad
China
Colombia
Congo
Cuba
Denmark
France
Gabon

Gambia
India
Indonesia
Iran
Iraq
Ireland
Italy
Kenya
Kuwait
Laos
Libya
Madagascar

Malta
Mexico
Morocco
Niger
Oman
Romania
Samoa
Spain
Surinam
Sweden
Togo
Turkey

I	A	B	U	C	A	I	B	M	A	G
T	I	A	W	U	K	E	N	Y	A	R
A	N	I	R	A	N	I	H	C	P	A
L	A	D	N	I	G	E	R	R	E	I
Y	M	N	N	S	A	M	O	A	A	B
E	O	I	R	E	L	A	N	D	U	M
K	R	A	M	N	E	D	E	W	S	O
R	O	R	N	O	B	A	G	A	T	L
U	C	H	A	D	I	G	C	Y	R	O
T	C	A	M	N	A	A	U	B	A	C
O	O	B	O	I	N	S	T	I	L	I
G	N	F	R	A	N	C	E	L	I	X
O	G	Y	D	P	Q	A	R	I	A	E
S	O	A	L	S	U	R	I	N	A	M

9. In your dreams

Here's a dream of a puzzle – 30 words (31 really, as 'second sight' is two words) connected with dreams for you to find.

create
daydream
demon
fables
fanciful
farrago
fiction
figment
figure
flight

guess
hope
ideal
imagination
inspiration
invent
muse
myth
nightmare
omen

original
phantom
reverie
romance
second sight
seer
trance
vague
vision
yawn

T	N	E	M	G	I	F	N	N	P	I
R	H	U	F	L	E	E	O	W	H	D
A	E	G	L	A	R	N	M	A	A	E
N	P	A	I	U	N	O	E	Y	N	A
C	O	V	G	S	C	C	D	M	T	L
E	H	I	H	R	D	R	I	N	O	F
R	F	S	T	F	E	N	E	F	M	A
A	A	I	Y	A	I	V	O	A	U	B
M	R	O	M	A	N	C	E	C	T	L
T	R	N	U	I	G	I	T	R	E	E
H	A	O	S	S	E	U	G	I	I	S
G	G	R	E	E	S	P	L	A	O	E
I	O	R	I	G	I	N	A	L	M	N
N	O	I	T	A	R	I	P	S	N	I

10. Find the nursery rhyme

Hidden in this grid is a complete nursery rhyme – four lines of verse you are sure to know. Can you find all the words you need to write out the rhyme? Where a word is used more than once in the rhyme you have to find it in more than one place in the grid. You need 22 words altogether.

O	S	G	E	L	K	C	A	L	B	A
V	S	L	L	E	H	S	N	E	G	G
E	S	A	H	C	E	I	L	A	N	E
R	L	D	Y	D	A	L	L	I	I	S
D	F	A	I	R	S	V	K	L	T	Q
A	N	R	D	A	A	E	Y	C	U	U
I	R	A	U	N	M	R	T	I	O	I
R	A	C	H	E	A	R	T	S	H	C
U	E	N	H	M	N	E	E	N	S	K
O	N	E	D	R	A	G	R	W	O	K
H	I	D	O	E	R	R	P	I	H	C
E	A	C	E	R	U	O	Y	T	A	A
A	I	R	S	R	O	W	O	H	I	J
D	A	N	D	Y	F	F	I	E	L	D

11. Just the opposite

The 38 words in this list are just the *opposite* of the ones you want to find in the grid. If the word in the list is *bad*, the one you want is *good*, and so on. See if you can find the opposites of all these words.

attractive	gentle	simple
becoming	happy	singular
behind	intermittent	sour
bold	obscure	stupid
cheerful	obtuse	sturdy
closed	pertinent	tame
cool	plain	ugly
design	polluted	unassuming
distinct	reassuring	unseemly
fat	relaxed	unwilling
first	restrained	urban
friendly	ruddy	wrong
general	ruffled	

R	Y	H	S	A	L	F	P	O	W	Y
I	E	D	G	R	A	A	U	A	T	E
G	T	A	I	U	C	H	R	T	H	T
H	A	N	D	S	O	M	E	U	I	A
T	M	L	A	S	M	R	P	A	R	C
S	I	R	T	E	P	A	U	A	D	I
W	T	I	F	L	L	E	L	A	L	L
E	L	B	A	T	I	U	S	N	U	E
E	U	C	I	N	C	L	I	N	E	D
T	I	M	N	I	A	L	V	V	E	E
D	I	E	T	O	T	C	E	A	R	T
D	P	R	O	P	E	R	U	V	I	O
O	A	C	C	I	D	E	N	T	E	N
P	P	L	U	R	A	L	U	G	E	R

12. Star names

Here are the first names of 28 well-known actors and actresses – you've seen them on television or in films. Can you find their surnames in the grid?

Alec	Jack	Richard
Brooke	Jane	Ringo
David	John	Robert
Diana	John	Roger
Elliott	Julie	Sean
Faye	Laurence	Sophia
Frank	Lee	Susannah
Gene	Marlon	Tatum
George C.	Michael	Woody
Helen		

A	L	G	I	E	L	G	U	D	Y	H
N	R	N	O	M	M	E	L	A	E	A
D	O	I	S	C	O	U	W	O	N	C
R	A	T	G	G	O	A	L	L	I	K
E	T	S	R	G	N	I	V	R	A	M
W	L	A	H	U	V	I	Y	R	C	A
S	O	A	D	I	B	R	M	O	A	N
I	V	R	E	N	E	N	R	M	R	S
N	A	R	A	N	O	L	E	A	E	K
A	R	L	N	E	O	F	D	L	T	H
T	T	O	C	S	N	A	F	S	L	S
R	C	R	O	S	E	R	O	O	M	A
A	N	E	T	H	N	E	R	R	I	M
O	D	N	A	R	B	Y	D	R	A	H

13. Germany – true or false?

Take your pencil for a trip around places in Germany — but beware! Some of the 42 names below are real German towns or cities – and some are just made-up names. Can you find them all and then guess which are real and which are invented? We have omitted all the accents to make it harder.

Artesin	Gemuten	Mashem
Augsburg	Goslar	Minden
Bing	Hamburg	Munchen
Bingen	Herren	Munster
Bonn	Kassel	Neuss
Borne	Kiel	Orborn
Bremen	Kleve	Osborn
Celle	Koln	Rucker
Currier	Laberg	Seesen
Darmstadt	Landau	Solle
Durce	Landsberg	Stuttgart
Emden	Limburg	Ulm
Ems	Lubeck	Worms
Essen	Luneburg	Zerhelm

N	G	N	M	G	H	G	G	L	A	N
D	E	U	E	E	R	R	R	W	R	L
B	A	S	R	U	U	U	E	O	T	O
O	Z	R	S	B	S	B	B	R	E	K
N	E	D	M	E	H	S	A	M	S	I
N	R	A	L	S	O	G	L	S	I	E
E	H	L	U	L	T	U	A	L	N	L
H	E	N	L	T	N	A	N	E	E	E
C	L	E	U	E	S	D	D	S	N	N
N	M	T	B	M	U	N	S	T	E	R
U	S	U	E	R	I	A	B	M	S	O
M	R	M	C	M	K	L	E	V	E	B
G	R	E	K	C	U	R	R	I	E	R
N	E	G	N	I	B	I	G	N	S	O

14. Just a matter of time

See how long it takes you to find these 38 words connected with time in one way or another.

ago	hours	semester
August	late	September
calendar	lease	shift
centenary	light-year	spring
chronicle	March	summer
crisis	May	sundial
defer	month	sundown
early	moonrise	teens
elapse	morning	timepiece
fall	nonce	was
February	once	yesterday
fortnight	period	yore
Friday	ready	

G	N	I	N	R	O	M	T	A	T	S
N	W	R	A	E	Y	T	H	G	I	L
I	O	A	T	M	M	U	G	S	M	Y
R	D	F	S	M	A	S	I	O	E	R
P	N	E	U	U	R	R	N	S	P	A
S	U	B	G	S	C	T	T	E	I	N
E	S	R	U	O	H	E	R	M	E	E
P	E	U	A	R	R	I	O	E	C	T
T	S	A	N	D	O	O	F	S	E	N
E	P	R	A	D	N	R	A	T	T	E
M	A	Y	E	R	I	E	L	E	A	C
B	L	F	I	D	C	A	L	R	L	N
E	E	S	A	E	L	D	L	A	G	O
R	E	Y	O	R	E	Y	A	L	C	N

15. To tell the truth

How quickly can you find these words of truth,
or words connected with getting things right?
There are 32 hidden in the grid.

accepted	learned	reliable
account	literal	revelation
accurate	nicety	rigid
attested	noted	seen
bald	perceived	statement
certain	probing	tenor
fact	process	tested
genuine	promise	tried
gospel	proved	truth
held	reality	verity
honest	register	

F	A	T	T	E	S	T	E	D	D	R
A	L	D	E	N	R	A	E	L	E	C
C	L	A	P	I	C	V	E	A	T	E
T	S	C	R	C	I	R	L	B	O	R
T	H	C	O	E	S	I	B	O	N	T
D	O	U	C	T	T	G	A	N	O	A
E	N	R	E	Y	A	I	I	G	I	I
T	E	A	S	E	T	D	L	O	T	N
P	S	T	S	N	E	I	E	S	A	D
E	T	E	S	I	M	O	R	P	L	E
C	R	S	R	U	E	O	M	E	E	V
C	U	T	E	N	N	E	H	L	V	O
A	T	E	R	E	T	S	I	G	E	R
S	H	D	T	G	N	I	B	O	R	P

16. Ifs and buts

See how many different words you can find which contain the letters IF or BUT, reading either backwards or forwards.

Y	E	T	U	B	I	R	T	N	O	C
R	A	T	I	F	Y	L	L	I	F	E
A	C	I	F	I	R	R	E	T	I	M
T	F	I	A	W	E	A	B	U	S	B
U	N	B	U	T	H	T	A	B	H	U
B	F	A	T	U	C	T	E	A	Y	T
I	I	U	R	D	T	R	L	T	X	A
R	B	Y	T	E	U	I	F	F	I	N
T	R	R	R	B	B	B	I	I	F	E
S	O	E	E	U	A	U	R	W	L	L
R	U	I	T	T	U	T	T	S	I	F
I	S	F	L	T	B	E	C	O	I	F
F	E	C	I	F	I	D	E	F	R	I
E	L	I	F	L	U	F	I	T	I	P

17. What do you know?

Here's a quiz to test your general knowledge – but you can find all the answers in the grid.

1. Warsaw is the capital of which country?
2. What are fish swimming together called?
3. What dance is associated with sailors?
4. What holiday do newly-weds have?
5. What is a lake called in Ireland?
6. The fourth letter of the Greek alphabet.
7. The simplest part of a chemical compound.
8. What word means satisfied and happy?
9. What sort of plant is the maidenhair?
10. What sort of play makes you laugh?
11. A sort of religious house.
12. What was the name of the last British king?
13. A meeting of cardinals to elect a pope.
14. The home of the International Red Cross.
15. Which alloy contains iron and carbon?
16. A wild animal with a striped head.
17. An army officer equal to an admiral.
18. Which bird might be an emperor?
19. Which city is associated with a tea party?
20. Which colour is associated with cowardice?
21. Which Dutch artist painted *The Night Watch*?
22. Which fish might be a rainbow?
23. A great Greek philosopher.
24. Which herb might be lemon-scented?
25. Which lizard has adhesive pads on its feet?
26. Which waterways are in Norfolk and Suffolk?
27. Which wind brings heavy rains in India?
28. An ancient purveyor of wisdom and knowledge.

D	E	P	U	T	Y	E	L	L	O	W
N	N	R	E	F	S	D	R	I	A	L
O	M	I	K	S	E	C	E	S	N	C
T	R	O	U	T	G	H	H	M	N	O
S	E	R	S	G	E	I	C	O	O	N
O	M	Y	E	T	N	E	T	N	O	C
B	B	I	N	G	E	E	I	S	M	L
A	R	O	T	A	R	E	P	O	Y	A
D	A	O	R	H	A	O	L	O	E	V
G	N	T	A	A	L	E	E	N	N	E
E	D	A	T	D	C	O	M	G	O	N
R	T	L	L	U	S	L	U	Y	H	E
T	E	P	L	O	K	C	E	G	H	G
D	E	E	P	I	P	N	R	O	H	T

29. Who is in charge of the restaurant kitchen?
30. Who lives in the far north of Canada?
31. Who owns land in Scotland?
32. Who stands in when the head is away?
33. Who throws the ball in a baseball game?
34. Who was the first president of the USA?
35. Who was the Norse god of thunder?
36. Who works at a telephone exchange?
37. Who works iron by hammering it?

18. Words of love

Have a romantic time finding these 34 words associated with boy meeting girl.

affection
amour
assent
attend
bride
caress
charm
dear
designs
distract
engaged
entice

entrance
fancy
fascinating
fond
friends
hers
honey
idolatry
loving
madonna
model

moony
mystery
nice
romance
scent
sentiment
softness
spooning
sweetheart
tenderly
yearn

A	S	S	E	N	T	F	O	S	M	Y
M	A	D	O	N	N	A	A	G	O	R
F	O	N	D	E	E	S	M	N	O	T
C	L	E	D	O	M	C	O	I	N	A
D	A	I	S	Y	I	I	U	N	Y	L
R	R	R	W	E	T	N	R	O	L	O
B	E	F	E	C	N	A	M	O	R	D
H	R	N	E	S	E	T	V	P	E	I
C	O	F	T	Y	S	I	I	S	D	S
H	F	N	H	R	N	N	I	C	N	T
A	A	D	E	G	A	G	N	E	E	R
R	N	I	A	Y	N	N	I	N	T	A
M	C	G	R	S	N	O	C	T	T	C
M	Y	S	T	E	R	Y	E	E	A	T

19. City liverymen

The City of London still has the ancient livery companies to which people of different trades belonged. Each comany had its own livery, or uniform, and you could tell a horner from a haberdasher by the livery he wore. See if you can find these 26 old tradesmen of the City livery companies.

actuary
armourer
baker
carman
cook
cordwainer
currier
dyer
farmer

farrier
fletcher
founder
gardener
haberdasher
horner
ironmonger
joiner
loriner

mason
mercer
plumber
saddler
skinner
waterman
weaver
woolman

N	S	C	U	R	R	I	E	R	M	R
F	A	R	R	I	E	R	E	L	A	E
L	D	M	R	E	N	N	I	K	S	C
E	D	R	L	E	I	S	S	I	O	R
T	L	E	H	O	R	N	E	R	N	E
C	E	H	J	E	O	U	D	O	N	M
H	R	S	V	O	L	W	O	N	A	R
E	C	A	N	N	A	A	R	M	M	A
R	E	D	B	I	U	T	E	O	R	F
W	A	R	N	I	N	E	K	N	A	A
R	R	E	N	E	D	R	A	G	C	K
E	R	B	P	L	U	M	B	E	R	O
Y	R	A	U	T	C	A	R	R	O	O
D	C	H	R	E	D	N	U	O	F	C

20. Names that make words

Half of the 32 words here are people's names or titles that have been made into words. The macintosh, for instance, is named after the man who invented a waterproof material for making it. Can you find the 32 words and then sort out the 16 words that have been made out of people's names or titles?

alien
ancient
aspen
aster
bloomers
boycott
braille
brolly
cardigan
chesterfield
dial

dundrearies
habitat
hansom
holly
lasso
lynch
macintosh
melba
priest
raglan
roses

sandwich
side
spell
talent
trellis
vandyke
victoria
watt
wellington
winner

M	A	C	I	N	T	O	S	H	E	R
O	S	I	D	E	A	E	E	W	K	O
S	P	E	L	L	L	T	I	E	Y	S
N	E	R	E	L	E	N	R	L	D	E
A	N	C	I	E	N	T	A	L	N	S
H	T	A	F	E	T	S	E	I	A	R
A	R	R	R	N	S	R	R	N	V	E
B	E	D	E	O	E	T	D	G	I	M
I	L	I	T	T	A	W	N	T	C	O
T	L	G	S	H	I	M	U	O	T	O
A	I	A	E	C	O	E	D	N	O	L
T	S	N	H	N	Y	L	L	O	R	B
T	T	O	C	Y	O	B	L	A	I	D
S	D	N	A	L	G	A	R	Y	A	M

21. Give a hand

Add the word HAND to BEFORE and you get the word BEFOREHAND. Put the word HAND before BAG and you get HANDBAG. Or put the word HAND between the letters SY and you get SHANDY. Get the idea? Then see how many words or sets of letters you can find that will make words if you add or insert the letters HAND.

T	O	P	H	O	L	D	N	A	T	S
U	L	L	I	B	R	E	D	N	U	P
B	E	F	O	R	E	E	N	W	A	R
I	M	A	D	E	G	L	I	A	R	I
W	R	I	T	I	N	G	H	N	G	N
R	A	T	T	L	E	N	E	A	N	G
O	E	S	K	E	D	I	B	M	O	O
U	M	E	R	C	I	S	E	Y	L	M
G	O	L	O	P	A	Y	L	L	E	B
H	S	O	W	A	M	B	O	O	K	T
T	R	V	I	C	R	A	F	T	I	R
S	S	E	N	I	F	F	U	N	P	O
E	A	R	L	O	U	T	L	A	S	H
F	E	I	H	C	R	E	K	A	H	S

22. On the air

Tune in here to these 25 local radio stations.

Beacon	London	Piccadilly
Capital	Manchester	Plymouth
Cardiff	Medway	Severn
Clyde	Mercia	Sheffield
Derby	Metro	Swansea
Forth	Norfolk	Tay
Humberside	Nottingham	Tees
LBC	Oxford	Trent
Leeds		

Y	A	W	D	E	M	E	T	R	O	A
B	R	E	T	S	E	H	C	N	A	M
R	C	L	E	A	D	L	R	I	E	B
E	A	P	E	N	Y	U	C	V	S	E
D	P	I	S	D	B	R	A	I	N	A
I	I	C	E	K	E	D	R	S	A	C
S	T	C	C	M	L	R	D	E	W	O
R	A	A	D	A	W	O	I	V	S	N
E	L	D	L	E	I	F	F	E	H	S
B	E	I	B	Y	V	X	F	R	T	H
M	E	L	C	E	N	O	D	N	O	L
U	D	L	R	T	R	E	N	T	O	N
H	S	Y	H	T	U	O	M	Y	L	P
T	M	A	H	G	N	I	T	T	O	N

23. In the country

See how quickly you can round up these 41 words that in some way suggest life in the country.

braes	grower	plum
copse	hayrick	prairie
cover	hen	river
cowshed	hollow	shop
dirt	horses	smith
ditch	incline	stream
down	loch	swamp
earth	lowland	tree
eminence	marsh	valley
fell	midden	view
fenland	moss	village
ferret	mountains	waggon
field	pasture	wood
geese	plains	

F	E	N	L	A	N	D	E	R	A	I
I	W	E	H	A	Y	R	I	C	K	O
E	A	H	H	F	B	V	R	R	I	H
L	G	R	O	W	E	R	I	T	T	T
D	G	A	L	R	E	R	A	R	P	I
I	O	S	L	V	S	T	R	E	A	M
T	N	O	O	L	N	E	P	E	S	S
C	C	C	W	A	I	L	S	L	T	W
H	Y	E	L	L	A	V	L	T	U	A
T	G	P	A	I	T	V	P	L	R	M
R	E	C	N	E	N	I	M	E	E	P
A	E	S	D	W	U	E	O	R	O	F
E	S	P	O	C	O	W	S	H	E	D
N	E	D	D	I	M	H	S	R	A	M

24. Anagrams again

Here's another set of crazy mixed up words for you to unravel. See if you can find all 31 of your new words in the grid.

a lie must
a time line
big Noel
bored war
count is
cur seen
gap in mac
gen out
get at Eve
his bop
lamer comic

Lee's pet
lenter
made PC
marginal
pass a net
pens go
pet device
pet lemon cat
plan it
put it rude

real ties
red tag
rest pop
set pile
sour gin
stamp store
tar Ali
tea scale
ten lines
tin rag

L	R	A	W	A	R	D	R	O	B	E
E	A	R	L	I	E	S	T	I	T	R
N	T	L	S	T	N	A	S	A	E	P
I	I	A	A	U	C	H	L	T	N	T
T	N	R	L	R	O	U	S	I	N	G
N	G	I	A	P	M	A	C	E	D	E
E	T	A	N	I	M	I	L	E	E	V
S	R	T	S	T	E	E	N	L	E	I
C	E	N	S	U	R	E	T	G	G	T
A	P	O	G	D	C	S	E	N	N	P
L	P	N	N	E	I	T	O	A	O	E
A	O	E	I	P	A	B	I	L	P	C
T	T	P	E	T	L	L	O	S	E	
E	S	T	E	E	P	L	E	E	N	D

25. How many animals?

No list this time – just see how many animals you can find in the grid. You're doing very well if you can find 20 and you're Mastermind if you can find over 30.

W	Y	A	K	R	A	V	D	R	A	A
A	M	A	L	L	R	E	G	D	A	B
P	C	L	A	Z	E	B	R	A	O	B
I	A	P	A	N	T	H	E	R	T	G
T	M	A	N	R	A	N	U	B	J	Z
I	E	C	T	T	E	A	N	A	E	R
N	L	A	E	F	T	T	G	B	J	E
I	A	E	L	A	N	U	T	O	A	G
H	H	O	O	R	A	G	U	O	C	I
C	W	G	P	R	H	N	R	N	K	T
U	A	L	E	O	P	A	R	D	A	A
P	M	P	R	G	E	R	B	I	L	P
A	S	S	E	B	L	O	K	A	P	I
C	E	T	A	C	E	L	O	P	E	R

26. The vowel's the same

See how many words of four or more letters you can find which do not use two or more different vowels in the same word. You can use the same vowel twice, or just one vowel – but not more than one. So CARAWAY and CART would be all right because they use only the vowel A, but not CARTER because it uses A and E. Get the idea? Then more than 40 words is very good and over 60 is brilliant. Don't forget a word like SWING also gives you WING.

S	A	L	A	D	N	A	S	L	A	B
P	P	O	I	I	A	U	P	U	T	U
L	O	O	C	M	R	R	E	P	S	B
A	S	K	O	I	I	E	T	U	E	B
S	T	R	I	N	G	T	R	S	L	U
H	O	O	T	I	H	P	E	E	E	H
N	C	I	S	S	T	E	L	E	C	C
I	N	T	O	H	C	N	O	P	T	T
G	D	N	I	H	A	A	N	E	R	A
H	W	A	I	W	R	P	N	T	D	C
R	E	L	L	I	T	S	I	D	N	T
A	L	I	L	A	E	R	E	S	A	I
Y	L	N	I	U	R	U	G	I	R	L
T	R	U	M	R	U	M	E	R	G	E

27. Get clued up

Find the words in the grid that fit the clues given here.

1. able to speak well
2. harassment
3. big meal
4. bird of prey
5. clear and precise
6. clergyman
7. country
8. difficulty in the way
9. disclose
10. dried white grape
11. evergreen tree
12. expelling saliva
13. food served in rashers
14. foolish
15. ghost
16. greeting
17. having been washed
18. highly enjoyable
19. interval for rest
20. in a quarrelsome way
21. joy
22. lady ruler
23. man-made fibre
24. marks cut in wood
25. person working in a stable
26. rage
27. ray of light
28. rogue
29. rude
30. someone in bed
31. something in the programme
32. syrup of pomegranate juice
33. way of holding yourself
34. written agreement

Y	L	R	U	S	U	N	B	E	A	M
L	R	E	P	R	O	B	A	T	E	E
E	F	V	R	S	E	H	C	T	O	N
V	N	E	R	U	T	S	O	P	O	I
I	F	A	A	N	A	A	N	I	R	D
T	P	L	E	S	U	L	T	A	N	A
A	L	V	U	L	T	U	R	E	Y	N
C	D	E	L	E	C	T	A	B	L	E
O	S	M	M	E	N	A	C	L	O	R
V	I	P	S	P	I	T	T	I	N	G
O	E	R	I	E	T	I	P	S	E	R
R	E	E	O	R	S	O	T	S	B	O
P	A	S	I	N	I	N	E	E	R	O
D	I	S	C	E	D	T	R	E	M	M

28. East coast main line

Travelling by train up the main line from King's Cross to Edinburgh you would pass through the 19 stations listed below, in the order given. Can you find them in the grid in high speed style?

King's Cross
Stevenage
Hitchin
Peterborough
Grantham
Newark
Retford
Doncaster
Selby
York
Thirsk
Northallerton
Darlington
Durham
Newcastle
Berwick
Dunbar
Drem
Edinburgh

M	E	D	I	N	B	U	R	G	H	R
R	A	B	N	U	D	R	E	M	G	Y
Y	B	H	O	T	M	A	H	R	U	D
A	B	E	T	H	I	R	S	K	O	E
S	L	L	R	N	O	T	S	E	R	N
S	A	N	E	W	A	R	K	L	O	E
O	I	I	L	S	I	R	H	T	B	G
R	R	H	L	D	R	C	G	S	R	A
C	E	C	A	E	E	N	K	A	E	N
S	T	T	H	E	I	R	R	C	T	E
G	F	I	T	L	O	I	N	W	E	V
N	O	H	R	Y	P	A	N	E	P	E
I	R	A	O	O	L	Y	B	N	E	T
K	D	O	N	C	A	S	T	E	R	S

29. Find the lady

Despite appearances, there's only one LADY in the grid. Can you find her?

L	A	D	D	Y	L	A	D	D	A	Y
D	Y	A	L	D	A	L	Y	A	L	D
Y	D	L	Y	A	L	A	L	D	A	Y
L	A	A	D	Y	A	D	A	Y	L	D
A	D	Y	L	A	L	L	Y	L	A	Y
D	Y	A	L	D	A	A	D	A	D	A
A	L	D	A	Y	L	D	L	L	L	A
L	A	Y	D	A	Y	L	A	Y	A	D
D	D	A	L	D	L	A	L	L	Y	A
Y	A	A	Y	L	A	D	A	L	A	Y
A	D	L	A	Y	D	L	Y	A	D	D
D	Y	A	L	A	A	D	A	L	Y	A
A	D	Y	L	D	Y	A	L	Y	A	D
L	A	D	A	Y	L	Y	D	A	D	L

30. Fighting words

Battle your way through to find these 32 words connected with fighting men, ancient and modern.

airman	marine	smiter
bowman	marshal	spearman
camp	melee	tactician
carbineer	militant	territorial
corporal	partisan	tiger
grenadier	prang	train
Gurkha	private	troop
hit	protector	trumpeter
mail	rank	volunteer
maim	redcoat	warrior
man-at-arms	scrap	

C	A	R	B	I	N	E	E	R	P	R
V	I	P	O	L	A	H	S	R	A	M
O	R	A	S	T	I	H	R	N	R	E
L	M	R	P	C	C	O	K	R	C	L
U	A	T	E	O	I	E	E	R	S	E
N	N	I	A	R	T	D	T	M	U	E
T	A	S	R	P	C	M	R	O	T	G
E	M	A	M	O	A	A	A	A	R	N
E	W	N	A	R	T	R	V	I	S	P
R	O	T	N	A	T	I	L	I	M	P
E	B	E	N	L	R	N	R	A	I	O
G	N	A	R	P	I	E	C	R	T	O
I	M	G	R	E	N	A	D	I	E	R
T	U	R	E	T	E	P	M	U	R	T

31. Are you sure?

Things are not always what they seem. People often get things wrong or are deceived. Here are 28 words connected with getting things wrong one way or another. See if you can get it right and find them all.

astray	fallacy	penalty
blunder	fancy	phony
camouflage	gulling	shadow
charlatan	guy	soft
cheat	hallucination	spoof
confuse	jest	whimsical
crime	mirage	wild
deception	mystic	wiles
delusion	oversight	wrong
device		

O	P	T	R	E	D	N	U	L	B	A
N	H	H	S	P	O	O	F	Y	H	S
C	O	G	O	E	M	I	R	C	L	T
A	N	I	F	Y	J	T	R	A	N	R
M	Y	S	T	I	C	A	T	L	A	A
O	E	R	E	P	E	N	A	L	T	Y
U	S	E	G	S	E	I	A	A	A	U
F	U	V	A	I	D	C	D	F	L	G
L	F	O	R	L	I	U	E	E	R	S
A	N	O	I	S	U	L	E	D	A	E
G	O	W	M	A	R	L	O	S	H	L
E	C	I	V	E	D	A	E	C	C	I
C	H	E	A	T	S	H	A	D	O	W
W	R	O	N	G	U	L	L	I	N	G

32. Rhyme time again

Here's another very well-known nursery rhyme for you to find. As before, all the words are in the grid. Words that appear more than once in the rhyme (like 'the' for instance) have to be found in a different place each time they appear.

C	O	U	N	T	R	Y	L	L	O	P
Y	O	J	O	H	N	D	A	E	L	A
R	P	U	I	N	T	U	R	N	L	P
N	E	M	E	L	G	T	O	D	A	E
E	U	P	U	H	L	C	O	C	H	R
H	L	E	E	H	T	H	E	T	E	O
T	B	D	L	R	A	R	I	V	E	A
H	A	N	D	L	C	W	O	D	S	M
E	L	D	D	I	F	H	A	P	H	O
Y	A	I	I	T	D	M	O	Y	S	T
T	S	U	D	T	W	O	C	P	U	M
H	S	N	O	L	N	O	G	E	C	O
I	A	G	R	E	E	N	N	E	H	T
N	W	O	R	B	A	T	T	L	E	S

33. Sevens up

How many seven-letter words do you think can be found in this grid? You'll do well if you can find 20, very well indeed if you can find more than 30. Have a try.

M	R	O	F	R	E	P	R	E	S	S
A	I	M	L	E	S	S	E	N	C	E
R	O	G	O	C	W	E	R	B	E	L
S	T	A	R	L	E	T	O	T	N	K
H	I	D	I	A	E	A	A	T	T	C
A	N	A	S	I	T	R	A	N	E	O
L	G	M	T	M	E	E	R	I	D	C
L	L	A	A	P	N	T	L	A	E	O
O	E	N	O	I	S	I	E	R	U	N
W	S	T	L	N	N	A	U	R	M	Q
B	N	T	F	G	O	S	L	E	I	U
R	U	L	E	E	N	I	W	T	N	E
O	O	S	R	E	V	R	E	S	E	R
W	C	O	C	K	A	D	E	F	E	R

34. Strange weather we're having!

If we had all this we'd have very strange weather indeed! See if you can find these 31 words connected with weather.

breeze
cirrus
climate
cyclone
damp
dark
drought
easterly
fair
gust
heatwave

hurricane
light
meteor
red
sharp
sheet
showery
sky
sleet
sun

temperature
tempest
thunderstorm
tornado
unsettled
warmer
whirlwind
wild
wintry
zephyr

R	T	E	Y	R	O	E	T	E	M	C
E	O	N	R	L	Y	S	E	S	K	Y
D	R	A	T	I	M	H	M	U	L	C
E	N	C	N	G	R	E	P	R	E	L
L	A	I	I	H	O	E	E	E	E	O
T	D	R	W	T	T	T	S	R	Z	N
T	O	R	S	L	S	U	T	E	E	E
E	R	U	T	A	R	E	P	M	E	T
S	G	H	E	R	E	I	S	R	R	A
N	F	W	I	L	D	R	H	A	B	M
U	A	C	S	O	N	K	A	W	P	I
S	I	T	H	G	U	O	R	D	M	L
Y	R	E	W	O	H	S	P	A	A	C
N	E	V	A	W	T	A	E	H	D	Y

35. Good for you!

It's good to succeed and be appreciated. Take a bow when you find all these 38 words associated with success and approval.

admired
applause
appreciate
approves
award
best
blessing
boom
cheer
deserve
dote
dream
endorse

esteem
garland
glory
grace
great
homage
immortal
love
laud
peerless
praise
premier
pride

prize
rave
regard
rising
roar
rouse
royal
shake
shout
supreme
sweet
treat

B	G	N	I	S	S	E	L	B	E	E
E	E	P	C	D	U	A	L	L	T	M
S	S	R	H	U	P	W	G	U	A	I
T	R	I	E	G	R	A	C	E	I	T
A	O	Z	E	I	E	R	R	S	C	R
E	D	E	R	I	M	D	A	I	E	E
R	N	L	P	E	E	E	I	A	R	A
G	E	A	E	S	G	G	R	R	P	T
S	A	T	E	S	U	A	L	P	P	A
W	S	R	R	K	H	M	R	O	A	R
E	V	O	L	A	A	O	O	D	R	O
E	A	M	E	A	V	H	U	O	U	Y
T	I	M	S	E	N	E	S	T	B	A
G	N	I	S	I	R	D	E	E	Y	L

Mazes and Trace-outs

This is the section where the puzzles take a different form and we change the rules for extra enjoyment. Numbers 36 to 40 are simple word mazes. All the words you want are in a continuous line and you find them by taking your pencil and tracing a line from one letter to the next, moving forwards, backwards, up or down, but *not* diagonally. All the letters in the grid are used, but no letter more than once.

The next five puzzles, numbers 41 to 45, are also word mazes, but in these lines can cross each other, and the trail can move *diagonally* as well as up, down and sideways, so they are a bit more tricky.

Finally, numbers 46 to 50 are trace-outs and these are a different kind of puzzle. You trace out each word or name, moving in any direction, including diagonally. But the words are not in a continuous line; you start again for each word and you can use letters already used for other words. But you may not go over the same square twice in the same word.

36. First a girl . . .

First a girl and then a boy, then girl and boy
alternately. Move up, down or sideways from
one letter to the next to trace eight girl-and-boy
pairs.

H	R	N	E	L	I	C	M	A	N	T
T	O	D	Y	L	N	E	A	S	A	H
E	B	A	M	I	T	J	A	S	C	H
Y	E	Z	I	L	A	C	M	E	R	A
R	L	I	N	O	R	W	E	P	L	E
O	R	G	E	T	M	T	H	H	J	S
G	E	A	R	E	A	T	L	Y	A	C
A	S	H	R	I	S	I	L	E	R	Q
M	O	A	M	T	R	O	P	H	E	U
T	H	R	G	R	O	T	R	H	L	I
T	E	R	A	E	B	S	I	C	E	N

37. African tour

You can tour 17 African countries by moving from one letter to the next, up, down or sideways.

T	S	D	N	A	L	I	B	A	E	T
O	W	A	S	W	A	Z	M	B	W	A
B	A	N	A	L	A	G	I	A	Z	N
B	I	A	I	L	I	E	Z	N	I	A
M	A	Z	R	E	B	N	E	S	U	S
U	E	S	T	H	R	I	C	A	D	A
Q	I	O	U	A	F	E	G	L	A	N
M	B	H	T	E	O	R	G	H	A	M
A	O	I	A	C	G	I	A	A	N	O
Z	P	I	Y	O	N	P	Y	O	C	R
O	M	A	N	E	K	T	G	E	C	O

38. Take to the trees

Thread your way through a thicket of 22 trees by moving from one letter to the next, in any direction except diagonally.

H	O	B	E	B	E	N	D	A	S	R
T	R	N	A	M	E	O	M	L	H	A
U	N	L	O	H	C	E	D	A	P	L
H	W	A	A	K	P	C	A	R	O	P
C	A	W	W	O	I	E	A	M	I	L
R	N	O	R	L	N	L	P	E	M	E
I	B	W	I	L	E	C	L	M	P	N
U	M	E	R	S	E	H	E	N	L	A
L	B	M	O	T	N	A	Z	R	O	H
R	E	A	C	T	U	H	E	L	A	T
R	Y	S	Y	F	I	R	L	B	C	K

39. Birds of Britain

Take flight with your pencil and trace out 19 birds of Britain, moving from one letter to the next in a continuous line, up, down or sideways.

H	E	L	O	R	R	R	A	A	W	S
A	W	G	W	P	A	K	L	N	O	N
R	K	A	E	S	T	P	H	E	R	E
O	N	W	T	H	N	A	S	A	T	H
B	I	R	E	R	U	E	R	C	N	A
T	I	G	N	H	S	K	C	O	R	R
R	N	O	L	S	W	A	E	P	M	O
A	S	W	D	F	I	L	L	D	O	O
M	L	I	F	T	N	C	O	W	D	W
U	L	S	G	W	P	H	L	B	R	I
G	A	E	N	I	A	L	A	C	K	B

40. City rover

Travel around 15 of Britain's cities by moving from one letter to the next, up, down or sideways.

L	I	S	N	O	L	L	E	I	F	F
R	A	L	D	O	L	D	B	S	H	E
D	C	E	B	N	L	I	R	L	P	R
R	O	F	R	H	U	S	T	O	O	E
I	C	D	A	R	N	L	O	L	I	V
E	E	S	T	E	O	I	R	H	T	U
L	F	F	I	T	T	B	M	Y	M	O
R	D	I	N	G	G	N	I	L	P	E
A	S	E	H	H	H	A	N	E	W	L
C	T	N	C	A	G	M	W	O	C	T
R	E	A	M	M	L	A	S	G	A	S

41. Sparkle with jewels

Here's your chance to sparkle! Trace out 18 jewels or precious stones in the diagram, moving from one letter to the next in any direction – including diagonally this time.

R	L	A	G	U	R	D	A	M	N	S
A	E	A	T	B	E	J	D	O	O	T
L	P	R	Y	E	D	A	N	L	N	O
Y	A	B	N	J	I	N	O	E	A	E
G	R	E	A	E	L	E	C	M	M	R
T	Y	M	E	S	T	N	R	O	A	E
S	A	H	T	P	A	T	N	Y	X	I
E	O	I	H	Q	E	O	U	I	Z	D
N	R	T	U	P	R	E	R	R	N	A
E	L	S	P	A	S	A	S	Q	P	E
B	O	O	D	A	M	I	O	U	O	T

42. Get plugged in

Get plugged in and switched on to find 13 electrical appliances, moving from one letter to the next in any direction including diagonally.

E	R	T	A	R	E	D	E	R	O	I
K	O	P	W	R	E	T	R	F	R	D
C	O	D	E	A	C	O	S	O	O	A
R	E	I	R	S	O	O	A	D	C	O
L	E	T	H	N	T	R	I	K	M	L
B	U	T	E	I	N	R	I	I	C	L
M	E	L	A	G	O	D	X	G	I	A
N	H	C	E	M	T	A	R	E	N	T
I	E	V	R	A	T	E	E	E	R	A
R	I	F	I	I	R	C	R	H	M	E
O	N	S	G	E	A	V	U	U	L	C

43. Lines of colour

Make this a colourful line-up by moving from one letter to the next in any direction, including diagonally, to spell out 20 colours.

M	O	N	R	P	U	A	U	N	L	C
E	P	E	L	C	V	M	O	V	A	I
Y	L	U	B	A	E	E	R	F	E	L
V	N	C	R	M	A	E	N	F	A	S
A	R	N	E	P	M	U	L	D	D	N
I	S	O	L	N	I	R	B	I	E	I
R	M	E	I	L	E	L	D	G	A	R
A	T	R	S	I	O	V	O	G	T	M
M	A	L	O	C	N	G	E	E	W	Y
A	O	N	U	E	A	G	L	N	E	O
R	N	G	E	E	R	R	A	T	L	L

44. Hello USA

Tour through 15 states of the USA, moving from one letter to the next in any direction until you have covered every square just once. To give you a start, the first state is Ohio.

H	C	A	S	N	I	N	G	I	O	A
U	W	A	O	S	I	L	Z	T	R	N
N	S	I	S	H	A	P	L	O	N	I
O	G	E	S	M	O	E	N	I	A	I
E	T	O	K	I	N	O	T	A	S	G
T	R	R	N	N	H	X	E	A	A	R
S	O	E	S	N	A	G	S	V	I	I
L	T	Y	N	Y	E	S	E	N	R	G
A	O	W	A	A	L	S	A	O	A	I
U	I	I	E	V	C	A	S	K	N	O
I	S	N	A	N	E	E	L	I	F	R

45. Seven dates

The date of the battle of Hastings, 1066, can be spelt out as TEN SIXTY SIX. In the same way seven other dates have been spelt out in this grid: 1498, Columbus discovered the mainland of America; 1588, the Spanish Armada defeated; 1666, the great fire of London; 1789, the French Revolution; 1851, the Great Exhibition in the Crystal Place, London; 1917, the Russian Revolution; 1945, end of the Second World War. Can you trace them out, moving from letter to letter in any direction, including diagonally? Tricky one this, so we've shown you where to start.

N	E	Y	S	I	X	S	E	N	I	F
S	T	E	E	T	E	I	E	F	E	T
X	I	E	T	I	G	N	I	V	T	E
F	N	X	F	V	E	H	N	E	E	H
O	I	T	Y	E	(F)	T	E	N	G	N
S	R	R	I	O	Y	N	T	I	E	T
T	T	G	U	E	V	E	E	I	E	N
E	H	N	I	S	E	Y	G	Y	T	E
N	E	N	E	T	N	E	T	H	N	I
O	E	N	I	I	N	E	T	I	G	E
Y	T	F	N	F	N	E	E	H	N	E

46. Men of music

Now we come to trace-outs, in which you trace out each word or name by moving from one letter to the next, up, down, sideways or diagonally. But the names are not all in one continuous line. You start again for each different name and you can use letters you have already used in other names — but *not* the same letter twice in one name. See how many names of well-known composers you can trace out in this grid. We can find 34.

When you've found all the names you can think of, turn to the answers for our list. Then see how quickly you can trace out the names in our list that you have not already found.

B	R	E	E	H	C	I	N	I	L	D
E	E	L	Y	O	P	C	S	U	E	S
T	R	W	G	E	U	S	O	S	B	I
E	G	A	Y	N	M	A	R	T	Y	K
N	H	N	D	I	O	D	O	G	S	T
E	D	K	L	Z	B	T	S	V	O	L
S	N	E	A	R	E	K	S	K	P	H
S	C	H	V	O	T	E	I	U	R	C
A	M	U	I	D	H	A	M	T	L	E
N	B	V	R	T	C	L	R	T	L	I
N	L	E	A	S	E	R	A	N	A	V

47. The kennel club

There are at least 31 different breeds of dog for you to trace out here. Move from letter to letter in any direction, including diagonally, and remember they are not in a continuous line.

Look at the answers to see the breeds you've missed – then turn back and see if you can trace out the missing ones.

E	E	R	I	P	O	M	E	A	P	S
V	I	N	U	O	D	L	N	R	E	T
R	T	G	L	B	E	C	M	I	T	D
R	E	L	O	O	W	R	A	H	E	A
E	Y	D	A	C	L	I	N	S	Y	L
P	R	H	S	H	F	X	T	E	K	M
L	G	U	O	I	O	F	E	N	A	D
B	A	N	H	E	R	R	S	A	T	P
H	R	D	R	I	G	A	E	N	I	E
W	U	A	O	R	L	B	L	U	K	T
W	O	H	C	L	E	X	O	S	A	M

48. Around the counties

Here's a trace-out that takes you around England. See if you can trace out 31 English counties here.

S	N	E	R	T	F	O	B	Y	N	E
O	H	C	E	S	D	R	V	O	S	R
R	U	M	B	I	W	E	R	A	H	I
T	I	W	A	R	R	I	M	V	R	S
L	H	S	E	S	U	H	C	P	O	M
T	M	Y	T	F	S	E	S	K	E	N
A	S	K	O	F	S	B	R	D	R	T
H	E	L	R	D	E	F	O	S	I	S
R	I	H	D	O	R	X	A	H	E	Y
E	U	N	C	L	N	O	C	N	L	T
D	A	L	E	V	E	W	A	L	Y	S

49. Pick the painters

See how many names of well-known painters you can trace out here. When you have found all the painters' names you can think of, turn to the answers at the back and see if you can trace out the rest of the 35 given there.

N	E	T	O	M	E	R	S	A	G	E
A	O	C	R	I	B	O	R	S	P	D
M	U	O	L	E	T	R	T	A	I	S
T	T	R	L	C	A	N	D	T	C	E
E	A	N	I	G	U	R	E	S	V	E
I	R	O	U	G	A	B	N	A	L	I
N	T	S	S	E	V	I	O	G	Z	L
T	I	H	W	C	H	G	R	C	Q	A
R	O	S	A	N	A	N	E	U	T	W
U	L	T	T	L	N	Z	R	D	E	R
S	A	E	R	E	A	R	C	C	N	E

50. Poetic goodbye

For the last puzzle, let's say goodbye with the poets. See if you can trace out the names of 35 poets here. If you get stumped look up the names in the back of the book and then see if you can trace out the ones you missed.

A	E	Y	K	O	R	D	S	W	P	E
T	P	I	E	O	Y	E	H	I	O	R
S	N	L	W	N	R	B	T	R	P	C
E	I	G	S	I	N	U	M	A	E	F
Y	D	T	A	S	O	G	N	E	S	I
O	U	S	M	D	O	N	T	N	P	E
N	C	A	I	L	A	W	E	S	C	L
E	H	O	L	T	H	K	L	T	D	O
R	U	C	E	S	G	E	O	I	T	R
A	G	D	R	F	D	N	C	V	E	A
L	Y	H	A	I	L	O	R	A	L	C

The Answers

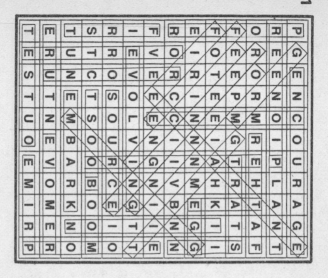

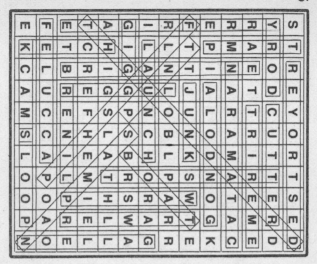

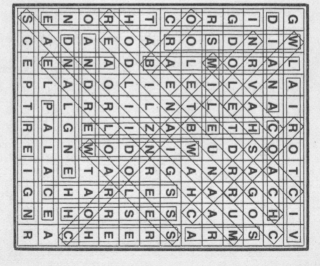

7

```
T S O C C A E S T W
I W N U Y L V G O E R
C E O R T O L A N L E
I D E E R G A E M O N
F M R P E R R A T I C
E E P L P E O O A V S
D A M E O P D R W R E
E N A N R A T N E N U
T I R I P S R M A B L
A N T S E T O R P R O
R G I H L O U N G E G
E R C U L R N N A A I
P R L B R A C K E T S
O V E R S L E I G H E
```

The hidden words are: operated, brackets, breath, conga, orchestra, accost, article, trounce, lucre, deficit, meagre, lounge, eulogise, grandee, replenish, sleigh, strain, spirit, altered, violet, meaning, bloomers, impersonate, renew, approve, property, ortolan, repast, erratic, agreed, pergola, protest, outgrown, pastoral.

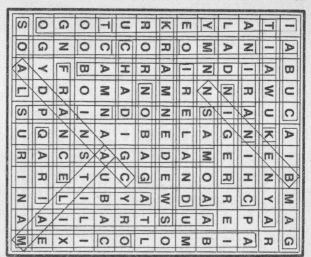

10

O	S	G	E	L	K	C	A	L	B	A
V	S	L	L	E	H	S	N	E	G	G
E	S	A	H	C	E	I	L	A	N	E
R	L	D	Y	D	A	L	L	I	I	S
D	F	A	I	R	S	V	K	L	T	Q
A	N	R	D	A	A	E	Y	C	U	U
I	R	A	U	N	M	R	T	I	O	I
R	A	C	H	E	A	R	T	S	H	C
U	E	N	H	M	N	E	E	N	S	K
O	N	E	D	R	A	G	R	W	O	K
H	I	D	O	E	R	R	P	I	H	C
E	A	C	E	R	U	O	Y	T	A	A
A	I	R	S	R	O	W	O	H	I	J
D	A	N	D	Y	F	F	I	E	L	D

Mary, Mary, quite contrary
How does your garden grow?
With silver bells and cockle shells
And pretty maids all in a row.

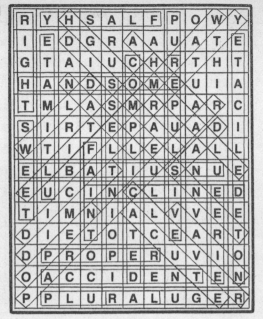

R	Y	H	S	A	L	F	P	O	W	Y
I	E	D	G	R	A	A	U	A	T	E
G	T	A	I	U	C	H	R	T	H	T
H	A	N	D	S	O	M	E	U	I	A
T	M	L	A	S	M	R	P	A	R	C
S	I	R	T	E	P	A	U	A	D	I
W	T	I	F	L	L	E	L	A	L	L
E	L	B	A	T	I	U	S	N	U	E
E	U	C	I	N	C	L	I	N	E	D
T	I	M	N	I	A	L	V	V	E	E
D	I	E	T	O	T	C	E	A	R	T
D	P	R	O	P	E	R	U	V	I	O
O	A	C	C	I	D	E	N	T	E	N
P	P	L	U	R	A	L	U	G	E	R

attractive/repulsive, *becoming*/unsuitable,
behind/ahead, *bold*/timid, *cheerful*/dismal,
closed/open, *cool*/warm, *design*/accident,
distinct/faint, *fat*/lean, *first*/ultimate,
friendly/hostile, *general*/particular,
gentle/rough, *happy*/sad, *intermittent*/regular,
obscure/noted, *obtuse*/acute,
pertinent/pointless, *plain*/pretty,
polluted/pure, *reassuring*/eerie, *relaxed*/tense,
restrained/flashy, *ruddy*/pale, *ruffled*/placid,
simple/complicated, *singular*/plural,
sour/sweet, *stupid*/clever, *sturdy*/delicate,
tame/wild, *ugly*/handsome, *unassuming*/vain,
unseemly/proper, *unwilling*/inclined,
urban/rural, *wrong*/right.

12

```
A L G I E L G U D Y H
N R N O M M E L A E A
D O I S C O U W O N C
R A T G G O A L L I K
E T S R G N I V R A M
W L A H U V I Y R C A
S O A D I B R M O A N
I V R E N E N R M R S
N A R A N O L E A E K
A R L N E O F D L T H
T T O C S N A F S L S
R C R O S E R O O M A
A N E T H N E R R I M
O D N A R B Y D R A H
```

Alec Guinness
Brooke Shields
David Hemmings
Diana Rigg
Elliot Gould
Faye Dunaway
Frank Sinatra
Gene Hackman
George C. Scott
Helen Mirren
Jack Lemmon
Jane Fonda
John Gielgud
John Travolta

Julie Andrews
Laurence Olivier
Lee Marvin
Marlon Brando
Michael Caine
Richard Burton
Ringo Starr
Robert Redford
Roger Moore
Sean Connery
Sophia Loren
Susannah York
Tatum O'Neal
Woody Allen

13

```
N G N M G H G G L A N
D E U E E R R R W R L
B A S R U U U E O T O
O Z R S B S B B R E K
N E D M E H S A M S I
N R A L S O G L S I E
E H L U L T U A L N L
H E N L T N A N E E E
C L E U E S D D S N N
N M T B M U N S T E R
U S U E R I A B M S O
M R M C M K L E V E B
G R E K C U R R I E R
N E G N I B I G N S O
```

The real German places are:

Augsburg	Hamburg	Minden
Bingen	Kassel	München
Bonn	Kiel	Munster
Bremen	Kleve	Neuss
Celle	Köln	Seesen
Darmstadt	Landau	Stuttgart
Emden	Landsberg	Ulm
Ems	Limburg	Worms
Essen	Lübeck	
Goslar	Lüneburg	

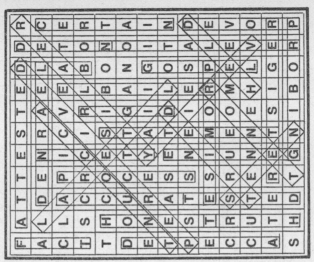

14

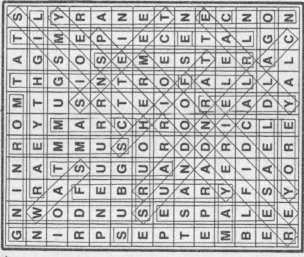

15

101

Y	E	T	U	B	I	R	T	N	O	C
R	A	T	I	F	Y	L	L	I	F	E
A	C	I	F	I	R	R	E	T	I	M
T	F	I	A	W	E	A	B	U	S	B
U	N	B	U	T	H	T	A	B	H	U
B	F	A	T	U	C	T	E	A	Y	T
I	I	U	R	D	T	R	L	T	X	A
R	B	Y	T	E	U	I	F	F	I	N
T	R	R	R	B	B	B	I	I	F	E
S	O	E	E	U	A	U	R	W	L	L
R	U	I	T	T	U	T	T	S	I	F
I	S	F	L	T	B	E	C	O	I	F
F	E	C	I	F	I	D	E	F	R	I
E	L	I	F	L	U	F	I	T	I	P

Here are 51 different words containing IF or BUT. Did you find more?

Abut, attribute, attributed, bath-tub, butane, butcher, butchery, butt, butter, coif, contribute, debut, edifice, fib, fibrous, fie, fiery, file, fill, filly, filter, fin, fir, first, fish, fishy, fist, fit, fitter, fix, fulfil, halibut, life, piffle, pitiful, protuberant, ratify, rebut, rife, rifle, swift, terrific, tributary, tribute, trifle, tub, tuba, tube, tubed, tuber, waif.

17

D	E	P	U	T	Y	E	L	L	O	W
N	N	R	E	F	S	D	R	I	A	L
O	M	I	K	S	E	C	E	S	N	C
T	R	O	U	T	G	H	H	M	N	O
S	E	R	S	G	E	I	C	O	O	N
O	M	Y	E	T	N	E	T	N	O	C
B	B	I	N	G	E	E	I	S	M	L
A	R	O	T	A	R	E	P	O	Y	A
D	A	O	R	H	A	O	L	O	E	V
G	N	T	A	A	L	E	E	N	N	E
E	D	A	T	D	C	O	M	G	O	N
R	T	L	L	U	S	L	U	Y	H	E
T	E	P	L	O	K	C	E	G	H	G
D	E	E	P	I	P	N	R	O	H	T

1 Poland	14 Geneva	26 Broads
2 school	15 steel	27 monsoon
3 hornpipe	16 badger	28 oracle
4 honeymoon	17 general	29 chef
5 lough	18 penguin	30 Eskimo
6 delta	19 Boston	31 laird
7 molecule	20 yellow	32 deputy
8 content	21 Rembrandt	33 pitcher
9 fern	22 trout	34 Washington
10 comedy	23 Plato	35 Thor
11 priory	24 thyme	36 operator
12 George	25 gecko	37 smith
13 conclave		

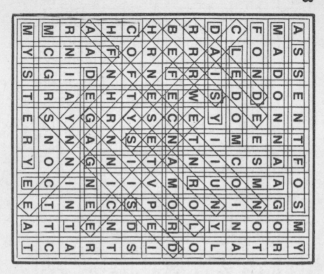

Puzzle 18 — word search grid

```
M M R A H C H B R D C F M A
Y C N A F O R E R A L O A S
S G I D N F N F R S E N D S
T G A E H T E E W Y D O O E
E R A G R Y S C E I O N N N
R S N A N S E N T Y M N A T
Y N N G N S I N A T C E F
E O I N I I V A N O I S O
Y C N E C I M O U N N M S
E T N E S C R L Y O Y
A T A R D S E I O R
T C A R T S I D O L M Y
```

Puzzle 19 — word search grid

```
D Y E R W R E H C T E L F N S
C R R R A E C E L D M A R R C
H A B E R D E H S H L E R R U
R U P N N B N V J H O R R R
E T L I I U N O E O R I I
D C U N N A L W U R E E
N A M D E T A W O D N R
U R B R K E R O O R I K
O R R G N O M N R I S R
F O O C A R M A N S O M
C O K A F A R M E R C R
```

20

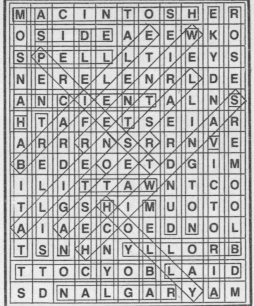

M	A	C	I	N	T	O	S	H	E	R
O	S	I	D	E	A	E	E	W	K	O
S	P	E	L	L	L	T	I	E	Y	S
N	E	R	E	L	E	N	R	L	D	E
A	N	C	I	E	N	T	A	L	N	S
H	T	A	F	E	T	S	E	I	A	R
A	R	R	R	N	S	R	R	N	V	E
B	E	D	E	O	E	T	D	G	I	M
I	L	I	T	T	A	W	N	T	C	O
T	L	G	S	H	I	M	U	O	T	O
A	I	A	E	C	O	E	D	N	O	L
T	S	N	H	N	Y	L	L	O	R	B
T	T	O	C	Y	O	B	L	A	I	D
S	D	N	A	L	G	A	R	Y	A	M

The words from names are:

bloomers
boycott
braille
cardigan
chesterfield
dundrearies

hansom
lynch
macintoch
melba
raglan

sandwich
vandyke
victoria
watt
wellington

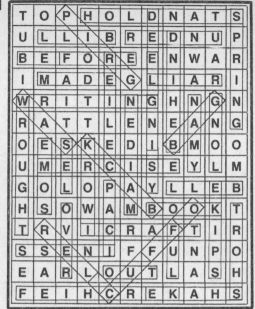

We found 47. Did you find any others?

Backhand, beforehand, behindhand, chandelier, chandler, forehand, handbag, handbell, handbill, handbook, handcuff, handful, handgrip, handhold, handicap, handicraft, handier, handiness, handing, handiwork, handkerchief, handle, handler, handmade, handmaiden, handout, handover, handrail, handsaw, handsel, handshake, handsome, handspike, handspring, handstand, handwriting, handwrought, handy, handyman, longhand, merchandise, offhand, overhand, shandy, shorthand, singlehanded, underhand.

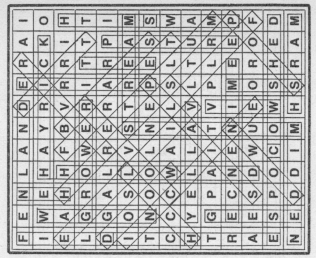

23

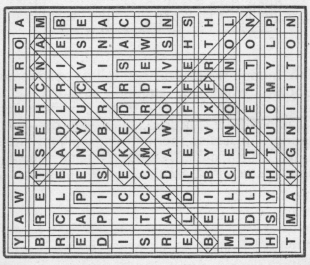

22

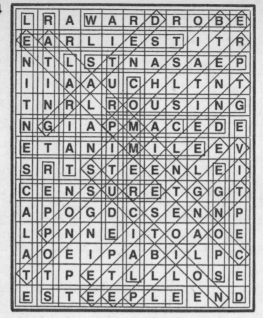

The hidden words are: simulate, eliminate, ignoble, wardrobe, suction, censure, campaign, tongue, vegetate, bishop, commercial, steeple, relent, decamp, alarming, peasants, sponge, deceptive, contemplate, pliant, turpitude, earliest, grated, stopper, epistle, rousing, postmaster, lariat, escalate, sentinel, rating.

25

W	Y	A	K	R	A	V	D	R	A	A
A	M	A	L	L	R	E	G	D	A	B
P	C	L	A	Z	E	B	R	A	O	B
I	A	P	A	N	T	H	E	R	T	G
T	M	A	N	R	A	N	U	B	J	Z
I	E	C	T	T	E	A	N	A	E	R
N	L	A	E	F	T	T	G	B	J	E
I	A	E	L	A	N	U	T	O	A	G
H	H	O	O	R	A	G	U	O	C	I
C	W	G	P	R	H	N	R	N	K	T
U	A	L	E	O	P	A	R	D	A	A
P	M	P	R	G	E	R	B	I	L	P
A	S	S	E	B	L	O	K	A	P	I
C	E	T	A	C	E	L	O	P	E	R

Here's a list of 39 animals:

aardvark	cheetah	llama
alpaca	cougar	okapi
anteater	dog	orangutan
antelope	eft	otter
ape	elephant	panther
ass	gerbil	polecat
baboon	gnu	tapir
badger	goat	tiger
bear	horse	wapiti
boar	impala	whale
camel	jackal	wolf
capuchin	jaguar	yak
cat	leopard	zebra

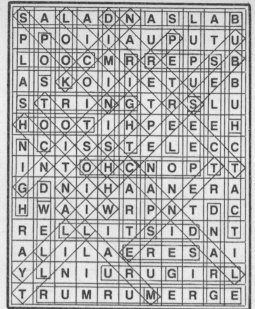

Here's our list of 66. How many did you find?

Alarm, alas, arts, balsa, beseech, cart, catch, chill, chilly, cool, cots, dart, darts, diminish, distil, dwell, elect, erect, girl, gist, grand, guru, hill, hilly, hoot, hubbub, itch, lilt, limit, look, lupus, merge, mill, murmur, naps, nick, nigh, nosh, petrel, poncho, post, print, printing, reps, right, salad, sand, sandal, scan, scandal, seep, select, sere, span, splash, spoon, still, string, tact, tens, tense, till, tosh, usurp, well, witch.

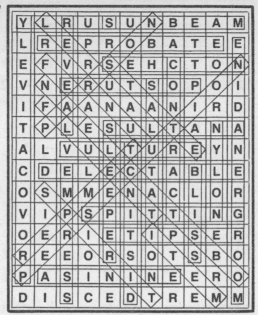

Y	L	R	U	S	U	N	B	E	A	M
L	R	E	P	R	O	B	A	T	E	E
E	F	V	R	S	E	H	C	T	O	N
V	N	E	R	U	T	S	O	P	O	I
I	F	A	A	N	A	A	N	I	R	D
T	P	L	E	S	U	L	T	A	N	A
A	L	V	U	L	T	U	R	E	Y	N
C	D	E	L	E	C	T	A	B	L	E
O	S	M	M	E	N	A	C	L	O	R
V	I	P	S	P	I	T	T	I	N	G
O	E	R	I	E	T	I	P	S	E	R
R	E	E	O	R	S	O	T	S	B	O
P	A	S	I	N	I	N	E	E	R	O
D	I	S	C	E	D	T	R	E	M	M

1 fluent	13 bacon	24 notches
2 persecution	14 asinine	25 groom
3 feast	15 spirit	26 temper
4 vulture	16 salutation	27 sunbeam
5 distinct	17 clean	28 reprobate
6 parson	18 delectable	29 surly
7 state	19 respite	30 sleeper
8 obstacle	20 provocatively	31 item
9 reveal	21 bliss	32 grenadine
10 sultana	22 empress	33 posture
11 laurel	23 nylon	34 contract
12 spitting		

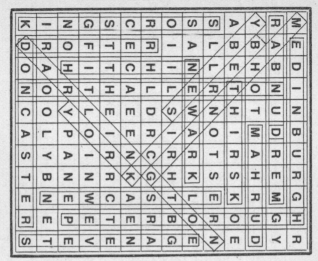

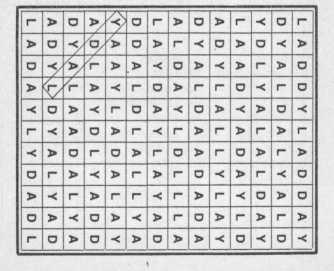

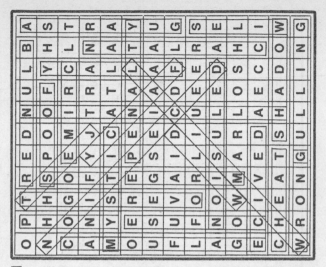

31

30

C	O	U	N	T	R	Y	L	L	O	P
Y	O	J	O	H	N	D	A	E	L	A
R	P	U	I	N	T	U	R	N	L	P
N	E	M	E	L	G	T	O	D	A	E
E	U	P	U	H	L	C	O	C	H	R
H	L	E	E	H	T	H	E	T	E	O
T	B	D	L	R	A	R	I	V	E	A
H	A	N	D	L	C	W	O	D	S	M
E	L	D	D	I	F	H	A	P	H	O
Y	A	I	I	T	D	M	O	Y	S	T
T	S	U	D	T	W	O	C	P	U	M
H	S	N	O	L	N	O	G	E	C	O
I	A	G	R	E	E	N	N	E	H	T
N	W	O	R	B	A	T	T	L	E	S

Hey diddle diddle
The cat and the fiddle,
The cow jumped over the moon.
The little dog laughed to see such sport
And the dish ran away with the spoon.

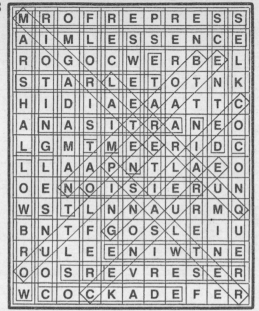

M	R	O	F	R	E	P	R	E	S	S
A	I	M	L	E	S	S	E	N	C	E
R	O	G	O	C	W	E	R	B	E	L
S	T	A	R	L	E	T	O	T	N	K
H	I	D	I	A	E	A	A	T	T	C
A	N	A	S	I	T	R	A	N	E	O
L	G	M	T	M	E	E	R	I	D	C
L	A	A	A	P	N	T	L	A	E	O
O	E	N	O	I	S	I	E	R	U	N
W	S	T	L	N	N	A	U	R	M	Q
B	N	T	F	G	O	S	L	E	I	U
R	U	L	E	E	N	I	W	T	N	E
O	O	S	R	E	V	R	E	S	E	R
W	C	O	C	K	A	D	E	F	E	R

Here are 36 seven-letter words. Did you find any others?

adamant	florist	reclaim
aimless	impinge	refloat
artisan	iterate	repress
boatman	lowbrow	reserve
ceiling	marshal	rioting
censure	migrate	scented
cockade	noisier	servers
cockles	operate	shallow
conquer	outline	starlet
counsel	perform	sweeten
entwine	psalter	terrain
essence	quarrel	tingles

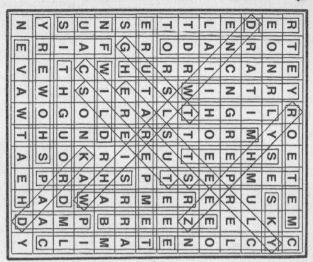

34

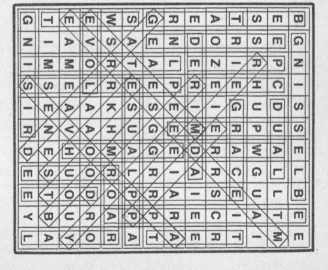

35

H	R	N	E	L	I	C	M	A	N	T
T	O	D	Y	L	N	E	A	S	A	H
E	B	A	M	I	T	J	A	S	C	H
Y	E	Z	I	L	A	C	M	E	R	A
R	L	I	N	O	R	W	E	(P)	L	E
O	R	G	E	T	M	T	H	H	J	S
G	E	A	R	E	A	T	L	Y	A	C
A	S	H	R	I	S	I	L	E	R	Q
M	O	A	M	T	R	O	P	H	E	U
T	H	R	G	R	O	T	R	H	L	I
T	E	R	A	E	B	S	I	C	E	N

Phyllis	Robert
Margaret	Thomas
Harriet	Matthew
Caroline	Gregory
Elizabeth	Rodney
Millicent	James
Samantha	Charles
Jacqueline	Christopher

T	S	D	N	A	L	I	B	A	E	T
O	W	A	S	W	A	Z	M	B	W	A
B	A	N	A	L	A	G	I	A	Z	N
B	I	A	I	L	I	E	Ⓩ	N	I	A
M	A	Z	R	E	B	N	E	S	U	S
U	E	S	T	H	R	I	C	A	D	A
Q	I	O	U	A	F	E	G	L	A	N
M	B	H	T	E	O	R	G	H	A	M
A	O	I	A	C	G	I	A	A	N	O
Z	P	I	Y	O	N	P	Y	O	C	R
O	M	A	N	E	K	T	G	E	C	O

Zimbabwe	Egypt	Senegal
Tanzania	Kenya	Liberia
Sudan	Congo	Zambia
Algeria	Ethiopia	Botswana
Ghana	Mozambique	Swaziland
Morocco	South Africa	

38

H	O	B	E	B	E	N	D	A	S	R
T	R	N	A	M	E	O	M	L	H	A
U	N	L	O	H	C	E	D	A	P	L
H	W	A	A	K	P	C	A	R	O	P
C	A	W	W	O	I	E	A	M	I	L
R	N	O	R	L	N	L	P	E	M	E
I	B	W	I	L	E	C	L	M	P	N
U	Ⓜ	E	R	S	E	H	E	N	L	A
L	B	M	O	T	N	A	Z	R	O	H
R	E	A	C	T	U	H	E	L	A	T
R	Y	S	Y	F	I	R	L	B	C	K

mulberry   oak   plane
sycamore   pine   lime
willow   chestnut   maple
rowan   fir   cedar
birch   hazel   almond
walnut   blackthorn   ash
hornbeam   elm   poplar
beech

H	E	L	O	R	R	A	A	W	S
A	W	G	W	P	A	K	L	N	O	N
R	K	A	E	S	T	P	H	E	R	E
O	N	W	(T)	H	N	A	S	A	T	H
B	I	R	E	R	U	E	R	C	N	A
T	I	G	N	H	S	K	C	O	R	R
R	N	O	L	S	W	A	E	P	M	O
A	S	W	D	F	I	L	L	D	O	O
M	L	I	F	T	N	C	O	W	D	W
U	L	S	G	W	P	H	L	B	R	I
G	A	E	N	I	A	L	A	C	K	B

thrush	lark	wren
swallow	pheasant	goldfinch
blackbird	sparrow	lapwing
woodpecker	eagle	seagull
cormorant	hawk	martin
heron	robin	swift
swan		

40

L	I	S	N	O	L	L	E	I	F	F
R	A	L	D	O	L	D	B	S	H	E
D	C	E	B	N	L	I	R	L	P	R
R	O	F	R	H	U	S	T	O	O	E
I	C	D	A	R	N	L	O	L	I	V
E	E	S	T	E	O	I	R	H	T	U
L	F	F	I	T	T	Ⓑ	M	Y	M	O
R	D	I	N	G	G	N	I	L	P	E
A	S	E	H	H	H	A	N	E	W	L
C	T	N	C	A	G	M	W	O	C	T
R	E	A	M	M	L	A	S	G	A	S

Birmingham   Sheffield   Leicester
Glasgow   Bristol   Hull
Newcastle   Nottingham   London
Plymouth   Manchester   Bradford
Liverpool   Cardiff   Carlisle

41

```
R L A G U R D A M N S
A E A T B E J D O O T
L P R Y E D A N L N O
Y A B N J I N O E A E
G R E A E L E C M M R
T Y M E S T N R O A E
S A H T P (A) T N Y X I
E O I H Q E O U I Z D
N R T U P R E R R N A
E L S P A S A S Q P E
B O O D A M I O U O T
```

aquamarine	amethyst	cornelian
topaz	garnet	jade
diamond	turquoise	ruby
jasper	onyx	beryl
sapphire	emerald	pearl
bloodstone	moonstone	agate

42

E	R	T	A	R	E	D	E	R	O	I
K	O	P	W	R	E	T	R	F	R	D
C	O	D	E	A	C	O	S	O	O	A
R	E	I	R	S	O	O	A	D	C	O
L	E	Ⓣ	H	N	T	R	I	K	M	L
B	U	T	E	I	N	R	I	I	C	L
M	E	L	A	G	O	D	X	G	I	A
N	H	C	E	M	T	A	R	E	N	T
I	E	V	R	A	T	E	E	E	R	A
R	I	F	I	I	R	C	R	H	M	E
O	N	S	G	E	A	V	U	U	L	C

television
refrigerator
toaster
washing
  machine
tumble drier

cooker
tape-
  recorder
radio
food mixer

heater
vacuum
  cleaner
digital clock
iron

43

M	O	N	R	P	U	A	U	N	L	C
E	Ⓟ	E	L	C	V	M	O	V	A	I
Y	L	U	B	A	E	E	R	F	E	L
V	N	C	R	M	A	E	N	F	A	S
A	R	N	E	P	M	U	L	D	D	N
I	S	O	L	N	I	R	B	I	E	I
R	M	E	I	E	L	D	G	A	R
A	T	R	S	I	O	V	O	G	T	M
M	A	L	O	C	N	G	E	E	W	Y
A	O	N	U	E	A	G	L	N	E	O
R	N	G	E	E	R	R	A	T	L	L

purple	ultramarine	blue
scarlet	crimson	amber
yellow	navy	puce
magenta	lemon	mauve
green	lavender	saffron
vermilion	indigo	lilac
orange	gold	

44

H	C	A	S	N	I	N	G	I	O	A
U	W	A	O	S	I	L	Z	T	R	N
N	S	I	S	H	A	P	L	O	N	I
O	G	E	S	M	O	E	N	I	A	I
E	T	O	K	I	N	◎	T	A	S	G
T	R	R	N	N	H	X	E	A	A	R
S	O	E	S	N	A	G	S	V	I	I
L	T	Y	N	Y	E	S	E	N	R	G
A	O	W	A	A	L	S	A	O	A	I
U	I	I	E	V	C	A	S	K	N	O
I	S	N	A	N	E	E	L	I	F	R

Ohio	Louisiana	Washington
Pennsylvania	California	Arizona
Tennessee	Kansas	Texas
New York	Illinois	Georgia
Massachusetts	Oregon	Virginia

45

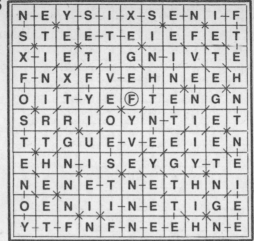

N	E	Y	S	I	X	S	E	N	I	F
S	T	E	E	T	E	I	E	F	E	T
X	I	E	T	I	G	N	I	V	T	E
F	N	X	F	V	E	H	N	E	E	H
O	I	T	Y	E	Ⓕ	T	E	N	G	N
S	R	R	I	O	Y	N	T	I	E	T
T	T	G	U	E	V	E	E	I	E	N
E	H	N	I	S	E	Y	G	Y	T	E
N	E	N	E	T	N	E	T	H	N	I
O	E	N	I	I	N	E	T	I	G	E
Y	T	F	N	F	N	E	E	H	N	E

46 Bach, Beethoven, Berlioz, Bizet, Brahms, Chopin, Debussy, Delius, Dvořák, Elgar, Gounod, Handel, Haydn, Holst, Mahler, Massenet, Meyerbeer, Mozart, Mussorgsky, Puccini, Purcell, Ravel, Rossini, Scarlatti, Schubert, Schumann, Sibelius, Strauss, Sullivan, Tchaikovsky, Verdi, Vivaldi, Wagner, Weber.

47 Airedale, Alsatian, beagle, bloodhound, boxer, cairn, Chihuahua, chow, collie, corgi, dachshund, Dalmatian, deerhound, Doberman, fox terrier, Great Dane, greyhound, Labrador, mastiff, Pekinese, pointer, Pomeranian, poodle, pug, retriever, Saluki, Sealyham, setter, Skye terrier, spaniel, wolfhound

48   Avon, Bedford, Berkshire, Cheshire,
Cleveland, Cornwall, Cumbria, Derbyshire,
Devon, Dorset, Durham, East Sussex, Essex,
Hampshire, Hertford, Humberside, Kent,
Lancashire, Lincoln, Norfolk, North Yorkshire,
Oxfordshire, Shropshire, Somerset, South
Yorkshire, Suffolk, Surrey, Warwick, Wiltshire,
West Sussex, West Yorkshire.

49   Botticelli, Canaletto, Cezanne, Corot,
Cotman, Cranach, Crome, Degas, Dürer,
El Greco, Gauguin, Giotto, Lawrence, Manet,
Millet, Monet, Murillo, Nash, Picasso, Pissaro,
Rembrandt, Renoir, Rouault, Rousseau, Rubens,
Tintoretto, Tissot, Titian, Turner, Utrillo, Van
Gogh, Velazquez, Watteau, Watts, Whistler.

50   Arnold, Auden, Austin, Brooke, Browning,
Burns, Byron, Chaucer, Clare, Clough,
Coleridge, Cowper, Dante, Donne, Eliot,
Goldsmith, Gray, Hardy, Kingsley, Kipling,
Longfellow, Lovelace, Masefield, Noyes, Owen,
Pope, Sassoon, Scott, Shakespeare, Southey,
Spenser, Swinburne, Whitman, Wordsworth,
Yeats.

More Beaver Books

We hope you have enjoyed this Beaver Book. Here are some of the other titles:

Mr Enigma's Code Mysteries A Beaver original. A cross between a detective story and a puzzle book, *Mr Enigma's Code Mysteries* presents eighteen baffling cases for you to pit your wits against, guided by master cryptanalyst Mr Enigma. Written by Tim Healey and illustrated by David Mostyn

Amazing Facts About the Living World A Beaver original. Did you know that some plants eat animals, that chameleons can look in different directions at the same time, or that an electric eel produces enough electricity to power a light bulb? A fascinating collection of facts written by Derek Hall and illustrated with line drawings and cartoons

The Beaver Book of Adventure Stories A Beaver original. A thrilling collection for older readers by authors such as Jack London, Robert Louis Stevenson and William Golding, with a specially-written contribution by the compiler, Raymond Wilson. Illustrated by Peter Dennis

These and many other Beavers are available from your local bookshop or newsagent, or can be ordered direct from: Hamlyn Paperback Cash Sales, PO Box 11, Falmouth, Cornwall TR10 9EN. Send a cheque or postal order made payable to the Hamlyn Publishing Group, for the price of the book plus postage at the following rates:
UK: 45p for the first book, 20p for the second book, and 14p for each additional book ordered to a maximum charge of £1.63;
BFPO and Eire: 45p for the first book, 20p for the second book, plus 14p per copy for the next 7 books and thereafter 8p per book;
OVERSEAS: 75p for the first book and 21p for each extra book.

New Beavers are published every month and if you would like the *Beaver Bulletin*, a newsletter which tells you about new books and gives a complete list of titles and prices, send a large stamped addressed envelope to:

Beaver Bulletin
The Hamlyn Group
Astronaut House
Feltham
Middlesex TW14 9AR

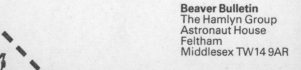

205126